The Open University

Open Mathematics

Unit 1

Mathematics everywhere

MU120 course units were produced by the following team:

Gaynor Arrowsmith (Course Manager)

Mike Crampin (Author)

Margaret Crowe (Course Manager)

Fergus Daly (Academic Editor)

Judith Daniels (Reader)

Chris Dillon (Author)

Judy Ekins (Chair and Author)

John Fauvel (Academic Editor)

Barrie Galpin (Author and Academic Editor)

Alan Graham (Author and Academic Editor)

Linda Hodgkinson (Author)

Gillian Iossif (Author)

Joyce Johnson (Reader)

Eric Love (Academic Editor)

Kevin McConway (Author)

David Pimm (Author and Academic Editor)

Karen Rex (Author)

Other contributions to the text were made by a number of Open University staff and students and others acting as consultants, developmental testers, critical readers and writers of draft material. The course team are extremely grateful for their time and effort.

The course units were put into production by the following:

Course Materials Production Unit (Faculty of Mathematics and Computing)

Martin Brazier (Graphic Designer)

Hannah Brunt (Graphic Designer)

Alison Cadle (TEXOpS Manager)

Jenny Chalmers (Publishing Editor)

Sue Dobson (Graphic Artist)

Roger Lowry (Publishing Editor)

Diane Mole (Graphic Designer)

Kate Richenburg (Publishing Editor)

John A.Taylor (Graphic Artist)

Howie Twiner (Graphic Artist)

Nazlin Vohra (Graphic Designer)

Steve Rycroft (Publishing Editor)

This publication forms part of an Open University course. Details of this and other Open University courses can be obtained from the Student Registration and Enquiry Service, The Open University, PO Box 197, Milton Keynes MK7 6BJ, United Kingdom: tel. +44 (0)845 300 6090, email general-enquiries@open.ac.uk

Alternatively, you may visit the Open University website at http://www.open.ac.uk where you can learn more about the wide range of courses and packs offered at all levels by The Open University.

To purchase a selection of Open University course materials visit http://www.ouw.co.uk, or contact Open University Worldwide, Walton Hall, Milton Keynes MK7 6AA, United Kingdom, for a brochure: tel. +44 (0)1908 858793, fax +44 (0)1908 858787, email ouw-customer-services@open.ac.uk

The Open University, Walton Hall, Milton Keynes, MK7 6AA.

First published 1996. Second edition 2000. Third edition 2008.

Copyright © 1996, 2000, 2008 The Open University

Edited, designed and typeset by The Open University, using the Open University TEX System.

Printed and bound in the United Kingdom by The Charlesworth Group, Wakefield.

ISBN 978 0 7492 2861 3

3.1

Contents

Study guide and introduction

This is the first of 16 separately-bound **units** which provide the main part of *Open Mathematics*. To study this unit, you will need the following course components in addition to this text:

◇ the supplementary booklet entitled *Readings* (for Section 1)

◇ a DVD player and DVD00107 (for Section 1)

◇ an audio CD player and CDA5508 (for Sections 1 and 3)

◇ the *Calculator Book* and your calculator (for Section 2)

◇ and, of course, paper and a pencil or pen.

Also connected with this unit are two television programmes, *Taking off* and *Wood, Brass and Baboon Bones*, the second of which is linked to a theme from Section 2.

The unit is divided into three main **sections**, some of which are divided again into **subsections**. You will find **icons** in the margin, at the beginning of each section or subsection; they indicate the particular components you will need, so that you can have them to hand when you study. More general advice about the different course components, and how to use them as part of your learning programme, is given in the *Course Guide*, which you should have read before starting work on this unit.

The diagram below shows how the sections link together. As this is the first unit of the course, you may find it more straightforward to work through the sections in the order presented, but it is possible to watch the video and listen to the audio 'out of sequence'. The horizontal bars on the diagram indicate the approximate time the course team estimates the sections will take to work through thoroughly. Each bar represents roughly one hour's work for an average student.

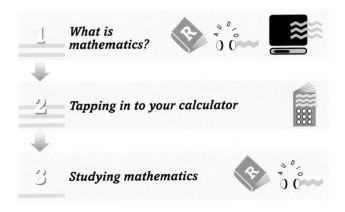

Summary of sections and course components needed for *Unit 1*

4

The icons used to represent MU120 course components

This unit is shorter than most of the others in the course. If you have completed the preparatory materials for MU120 you should find that *Unit 1* and the associated assessment work take about seven or eight hours of study. If you had to rush the preparatory materials you may find that this unit takes rather longer.

In order to help you keep your learning active and to enable you to become involved in assessing and evaluating your own progress, there are **activities** for you to do. Comments relating to most of the activities can be found at the end of the unit. As you complete the activities, keep your written responses filed carefully, as you may need to refer back to them later.

You are at the start of a journey full of ideas and exploration—of looking at things in different ways. It will involve gaining new knowledge and understanding about mathematics. This unit, *Mathematics Everywhere*, will get you started on that journey and will introduce you to the different course components you will use to explore mathematics. Along the way, you will also learn some mathematics using the calculator and so start to develop a feel for its use. Consequently, this unit is not like other units of the course—you will spend some time exploring the different course components and looking at your own study methods.

Having set out on her mathematical journey, Dawn suddenly remembered that she had forgotten to pack any sandwiches

For many of you this will be the first Open University course you take: so MU120 has a strand that encourages you to reflect on and analyse the way in which you are studying. Many students have found that these sections help them develop effective study skills which can be used throughout this course and beyond.

There are many reasons why people study mathematics and they gain a range of different benefits from doing so. For some, it provides a means of achieving greater understanding and insight into the physical world around them. For others, it is the social world of people and their concerns that is most in focus and of greatest interest. For some, doing mathematics is about sharing in an age-old human activity. For others again, it is curiosity about the inner, individual worlds of imagination and possibility. There is material for all these possible orientations in the course.

You, of course, will have your own interests and enthusiasms. As your mathematical thinking develops, both while you are studying the course and afterwards, you will be able to bring your enhanced mathematical understanding and skill to bear on different aspects of your life.

1 What is mathematics?

Aims   The aims of this section are to:

◇   help you clarify your own ideas of what mathematics is;

◇   give you experience of reading different types of written mathematics;

◇   give you an initial feel of how a mathematician views the world.

   ◇

You have chosen to study a course entitled 'Open Mathematics', but what exactly is mathematics? It sounds a simple enough question but, in fact, mathematics is not easy to define.

The Concise Oxford Dictionary defines mathematics like this:

> **mathematics** *n. pl.* (also treated as *sing.*) (**pure**) ∼, abstract science of space, number, and quantity; (**applied**) ∼, this applied to branches of physics, astronomy, etc.; (as *pl.*) use of mathematics in calculation etc.; so **mathemati′** CIAN *n.*

While Pears Cyclopaedia describes it like this:

> **Mathematics** is a body of knowledge expressed in a language of symbols. *Pure* mathematics studies the propositions that can be deduced in this language by applying definite rules of reasoning to sets of axioms. In *Applied* mathematics, the mathematical language is used, often with great effect to discuss problems of the real world, such as mechanics, statistics and science generally. In range, subtlety, complexity and depth mathematics is unsurpassed among the intellectual disciplines and its study has attracted some of the most brilliant men (*sic*) in history.

One of these 'brilliant' individuals, Jacob Bronowski, under the heading *The Music of the Spheres* wrote:

> Mathematics is in many ways the most elaborated and sophisticated of the sciences—or so it seems to me, as a mathematician. So I find both a special pleasure and constraint in describing the progress of mathematics, because it has been part of so much human speculation: a ladder for mystical as well as rational thought in the intellectual ascent of man.

However, not all scientists share the same enthusiasm for the subject. Carl Jung, the eminent Swiss psychiatrist, described his 'downright fear of the mathematics class' and went on:

> All my life it remained a puzzle to me why it was that I never managed to get my bearings in mathematics when there was no doubt that I could calculate properly.

Many people will sympathize with Jung's expression of his fears and lack of understanding. In Section 1.1, you are asked to consider your own feelings towards and understanding of mathematics—do you share Bronowski's enthusiasm or Jung's bewilderment?

1.1 Mathematics and you

Many people's ideas about what mathematics actually is are based upon their early experiences at school. The first two activities aim to help you recall formative experiences from childhood.

Activity 1   Carl Jung's school days

Read carefully the article, *School Years* in the Readings Booklet. As you read, look out for and make a note of any sentences which resonate particularly with your own experience of learning mathematics at school. It may be that you remember similar feelings or situations. Alternatively, Jung's words may spark off much more positive memories for you.

Before reading on, have a look at the Comments on Activity 1 at the back of this unit.

Notice that this was an **activity**: and so you were expected to be active. You were asked to **read** and to **make notes**. A good way of doing the latter in this case would have been to underline particular sentences in the Readings Booklet and perhaps to jot down some thoughts in the wide margin beside the text. Most of the course materials have margins like this and many students find that annotating the text, underlining, and marking key ideas are very effective ways of ensuring that study is active.

Bal was so delighted with his marginal annotations that he arranged to have them published in a hard-back edition

Activity 2 *Back to school*

Spend a couple of minutes thinking about your experiences of mathematics at the schools you have attended. Try to picture the classrooms, the teachers, or any of the individual lessons. Are there particular emotions linked to mathematics? Did any of your teachers affect the way you felt about the subject? Do you think you were 'good at maths'?

Summarize your thinking by completing the following sentence: 'During my school years, I came to see that mathematics was ...'.

Outside school, you will have moved on from *learning* mathematics to *using* it, perhaps consciously but, probably more frequently, unconsciously. For example, you may have looked at a statistical chart in a newspaper or on TV and subconsciously used mathematics in interpreting the meaning. You may have had to prepare a report which used numerical data. You will certainly have used mathematics when handling money, comparing prices, estimating the length of a journey (both time and distance), doing DIY jobs, following recipes, and so on.

Activity 3 *Everyday maths*

(a) Think back over the last day or two and try to identify as many occasions as possible when you have been using mathematics. How would you describe your level of competence with the mathematics that you were using?

(b) When was the last time you noticed that you were consciously thinking about mathematics? Did you do so with confidence?

The aim of the first three activities was to help you to answer the question 'What does the term *mathematics* mean to you?' Soon you will be asked to view a short video sequence that shows a collection of other people's responses to this question and others that you are trying to answer in this unit.

Video bands are used at various points in the course when it is the most suitable way of introducing some aspect of the topic being studied. Here are some of the reasons why video is used in MU120:

◇   to show events and places that cannot be easily experienced at first hand;

◇   to save time: for example, in presenting statistical evidence of a study that took over a year to complete;

◇   to provide dynamic visual images that aid learning;

◇   to allow you to collect otherwise inaccessible data;

◇   to provide motivation or trigger curiosity to help you work through a difficult topic;

◇   to add variety to topics by giving alternative viewpoints or approaches.

Viewing video for learning purposes requires its own set of skills. Video material is often intensive and needs to be worked on actively and not merely passively 'watched'. It is not a television programme for entertainment purposes. It is not 'moving wallpaper'.

Although watching a DVD or television programme may well be an excellent aid to memory, a video band for learning should not be used in isolation. Before watching, complete any preparatory work and find out what the video has been designed to do. As you watch and listen, try to think about the key points that are being made and how they relate to your understanding of the topic. Stop the DVD whenever you need time to think about a point that has been made. One strength of a DVD is that you can watch different parts again as often as you like.

In some video bands, concepts are built up by the rapid intercutting of visual images and such pictures can provides a powerful impact. However, the material being presented may represent just one of a number of possible viewpoints. Try to be critical—question and evaluate what you are viewing. Think about what may have been left out in creating the story, and whether this helps you to understand what is there.

So, to the practicalities of viewing video bands.

◇   Make sure that you can watch the video in comfort but that you are also in a position where you can make notes. Have a pencil and paper to hand.

◇   Try to ensure that you have enough time to view the band and respond to the sequence completely. For example, this first sequence itself lasts less than 15 minutes but you may find that you will need a clear half-hour to be able to view parts of it a second time and to do some writing.

◇   Make sure that you can easily stop, start and replay the DVD whenever you need to.

Activity 4   *Maths as others see it*

Band 1 of DVD00107 was recorded in the Whittington Hospital in north London. You will see a series of short sequences in which people respond to questions concerning their own views of mathematics. However, the video band also shows extended sequences in which three people (pictured below) talk about their work in the hospital.

(a) As you watch and listen to Trevor, Emma and Mark, make a note of mathematical ideas to which they refer.

- What mathematical skills and ideas do they use?
- Do you think they are consciously using mathematics?

(b) As you listen, make a note of any responses about people's view of mathematics which strike you as unusual or particularly interesting.

- Are the responses similar to your own?
- Do these responses seem to you typical of the population as a whole?

(c) When the band has finished look back over the notes you have made and check to see whether you have answered the questions above. If necessary view any parts of the video band again and add to your notes. Also think about the pros and cons of using video in this way.

Trevor Arnold, hotel services manager

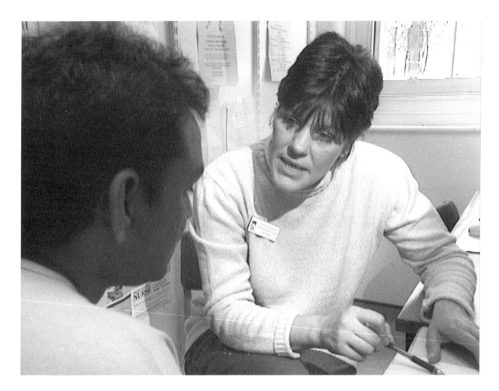

Emma Prescott, Thalassaemia nurse specialist

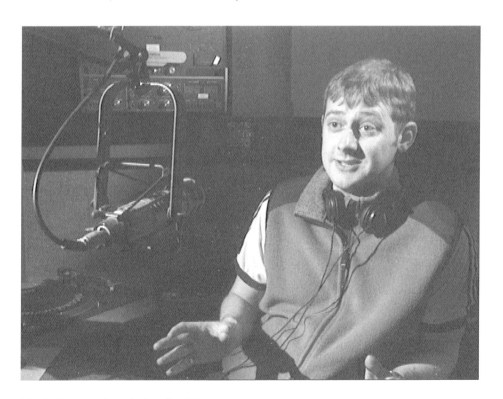

Mark Hanson, hospital radio DJ

1.2 Recognizing mathematics

In Section 1.1, you were asked to consider what mathematics means to you as you begin your study of Open Mathematics. No doubt by the time you get to the end of the course your ideas about mathematics will have developed and changed. In this sub-section, you will continue to think about the nature of mathematics as you look at four very different pieces of mathematical writing.

All four pieces of writing are instantly recognizable as mathematics. Some can be easily understood but others are much more difficult. Please do not worry about that for the moment. The four pieces of writing have been chosen with some care in order to make particular points about the nature of mathematics.

Activity 5   Yes, but is it maths?

On the next few pages you will see four pieces of writing labelled Examples 1, 2, 3 and 4.

In later activities you will be asked to read each of them in detail but for now spend no more than a minute looking at each one. Identify what it is that indicates that this is mathematical writing and decide what sort of mathematics is being used.

Before you read on, remember to look at the comments on Activity 5 at the back of this unit.

In the next activity you will be asked to look in more detail at Example 1. If you have been able to spend a lot of time on the MU120 Preparatory Material, this writing may be familiar to you. It is one person's response to one of the optional Brain stretchers in Section 1.4 of the *Calculator Book*. The question here is to investigate what meaning would be attached to the symbols 7^{-3}. Whether or not you have done this particular Brain stretcher, you should be able to make some sense of what this person has written.

It is clearly mathematical writing. There are numbers all over the page, along with other well-known mathematical symbols such as $=$, $\times$ and $\div$. Notice also the use of **powers**, the small digits written slightly above and to the right of the usual-sized digits. For example, 7^{-3} is read as 'seven to the power minus three'.

It is one thing to know how to read the symbols and quite another to know what they mean. What is shown here is an attempt to work out what 7^{-3} represents and how it matches what the writer already knows about powers. In *Preparatory Resource Book A*, Sections 4.2.1 (Power notation) and 4.2.2 (Multiplying and dividing powers) deal with the basic ideas about powers. This is probably one of the most advanced pieces of mathematics with which you ought to be familiar before the course starts, so if necessary have another look at those sections before you read any further.

The writing in Example 1 is an example of a mathematical **investigation**. The writer is not setting out to answer a well-defined question to which there is a single right answer. Rather she was working at an open-ended series of questions and aiming to increase her own understanding. Notice how she works from *what she knows* towards *what she wants* and writes relevant words alongside her working. There are indications of where she is stuck (look for the questions marks) and where she gets flashes of insight (look for exclamation marks).

For whom do you think the author of Example 1 was writing? It is likely that she was writing a response to the investigation mainly for her own benefit. She may well want to come back to look at this writing later and it is important that she will be able to follow her own thinking through again. Notice the way she has highlighted her conclusion. This is the thing that she wants to remember, the thing that, hopefully, she has learned.

Activity 6   *Investigating the investigation*

Take your time and read very carefully through Example 1, bearing in mind the points made above. Work through the mathematics, thinking about each line of the argument.

Keep asking yourself these questions:

◇   Do I agree with that?

◇   Would I have expressed that differently?

◇   Could I explain that to someone else in my own words?

Example 1 was a piece of so-called *pure mathematics*. Recall the definitions of pure mathematics given at the beginning of this unit.

> Pure mathematics: abstract science of space, number, and quantity.

> Pure mathematics studies the propositions that can be deduced in this language by applying definite rules of reasoning to sets of axioms.

In Example 1, there was no link to the real world. However, Example 2 is a very different type of mathematical writing. It is taken from a newspaper and uses mathematics to convey information to a general readership. It is therefore an example of mathematics being applied to handling data that arise in the real world. This particular branch of mathematics, known as statistics, is the main component of the first block of MU120, in *Units 2–5*.

Example 1

What is 7^{-3} ?   Try 7 $\boxed{\wedge}$ $\boxed{(-)}$ 3 , which is $.0029|545.$

But why?   *This is what I want to know*

Try:
$$2^{-1} = .5 = \tfrac{1}{2}$$
$$2^{-2} = .25 = \tfrac{1}{4} \quad (ah!)$$
$$2^{-3} = .125 = \tfrac{1}{8}$$
$$2^{-4} = .0625 = \tfrac{1}{16}? \quad (Check: 1 \div 16 = .0625)$$

So I guess:
$$2^{-5} \text{ will be } \tfrac{1}{32}$$
$$2^{-6} \text{ will be } \tfrac{1}{64} \quad (doubling \text{ the bottom number})$$
$$2^{-7} \text{ will be } \tfrac{1}{128}$$
$$2^{-8} \text{ will be } \tfrac{1}{256} \quad (Check: 2^{-8} = 1 \div 256 = .0039062s)$$

What's the connection between -8 and 256 ?

Ah! $2^{8} = 2 \times 2 \times 2 \times 2 \times 2 \times 2 \times 2 \times 2 = 256$ Yes!

So now I know $2^{-8} = 1 \div 256$

or $2^{-8} = 1 \div 2^{8}$

So what is 7^{-3} ?   Perhaps $7^{-3} = 1 \div 7^{3}$?

Check: $7^{3} = 343$

$1 \div 343 = .0029154519$ Yes!

So I think that 10^{-1} means $1 \div 10^{1}$ (i.e. $.1$)

10^{-2} means $1 \div 10^{2}$ (i.e. $.01$), etc

Perhaps in general

A number to the power minus something means 1 divided by the number to the power something.

Activity 7   *Packaging pictures*

Study each of the five statistical diagrams that make up Example 2. Write down, in one or two sentences, your interpretation of the information that each diagram displays.

Example 2

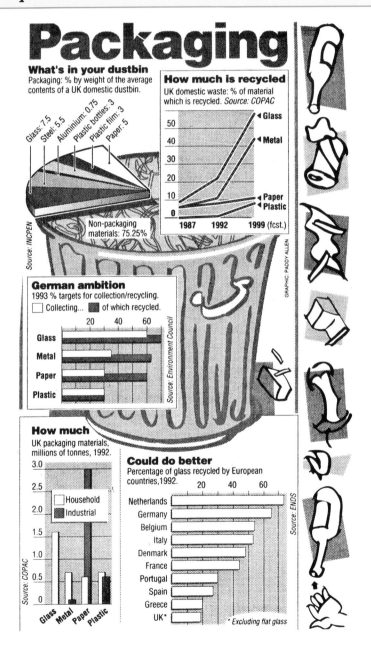

Packaging

What's in your dustbin
Packaging: % by weight of the average contents of a UK domestic dustbin.

Glass: 7.5
Steel: 5.5
Aluminium: 0.75
Plastic bottles: 3
Plastic film: 3
Paper: 5

Non-packaging materials: 75.25%

Source: INCPEN

How much is recycled
UK domestic waste: % of material which is recycled. *Source: COPAC*

◄ Glass
◄ Metal
◄ Paper
◄ Plastic

50
40
30
20
10
0

1987   1992   1999 (fcst.)

German ambition
1993 % targets for collection/recycling.
☐ Collecting...   ■ of which recycled.

20   40   60

Glass
Metal
Paper
Plastic

Source: Environment Council

How much
UK packaging materials, millions of tonnes, 1992.

3.0
2.5
2.0
1.5
1.0
0.5
0

☐ Household
■ Industrial

Glass   Metal   Paper   Plastic

Source: COPAC

Could do better
Percentage of glass recycled by European countries, 1992.

20   40   60

Netherlands
Germany
Belgium
Italy
Denmark
France
Portugal
Spain
Greece
UK*

* *Excluding flat glass*

Source: ENDS

GRAPHIC: PADDY ALLEN

16

Graphs and diagrams offer thought-provoking ways of displaying quantitative information. Often the most effective way of describing and summarizing a set of numbers is to use images related to those numbers. Of course, the newspaper could have chosen to represent the information about packaging using tables of numbers, but the diagrams are certainly more eye-catching and make patterns more obvious. For example, the UK's low percentage of recycled glass in 'Could do better' is shown much more clearly than it would be if only the numerical percentages were displayed.

However, like numbers, graphs and diagrams are abstract representations that summarize certain aspects of the world in a very condensed form. Unlike photographs which provide a 'true' likeness, their interpretation requires a degree of mental effort on the part of the reader. Although a picture may sometimes be worth a thousand words, a poorly-designed one merely obscures the underlying message.

The mathematical writing in Example 3 also uses diagrams but for a very different purpose. It arises from a particular three-dimensional puzzle, sometimes called a Soma cube, pictured below.

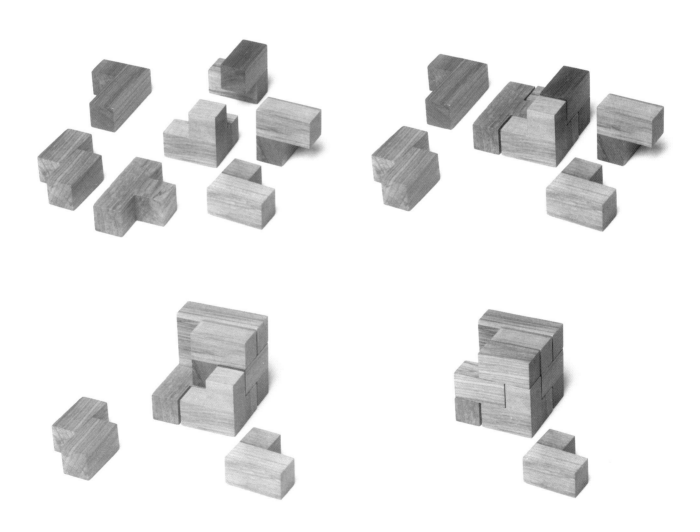

Piecing together a Soma cube

There are seven wooden pieces, which can be assembled to form a solid cube. The manufacturer of the puzzle claimed that there are over 16 000 ways of assembling the cube. The writer of Example 3 had found, by trial and error, several different solutions but was beginning to doubt the claim that there were as many as 16 000. The example shows the notes that he made as ideas crossed his mind about how to make sense of the manufacturer's claim.

There were two particular problems faced by the writer. First, what precisely is meant by a 'solution': what makes one solution different from another? Second, what is the best way of recording a particular solution: what notation is best to use?

Activity 8 *Does it make sense?*

Look carefully at Example 3 and try to make some sense of it. Notice that there are four bullet-points: try understanding each of these points separately, but don't worry if you find it difficult to follow. However, do make a note of the point when it becomes very difficult to understand.

Example 3

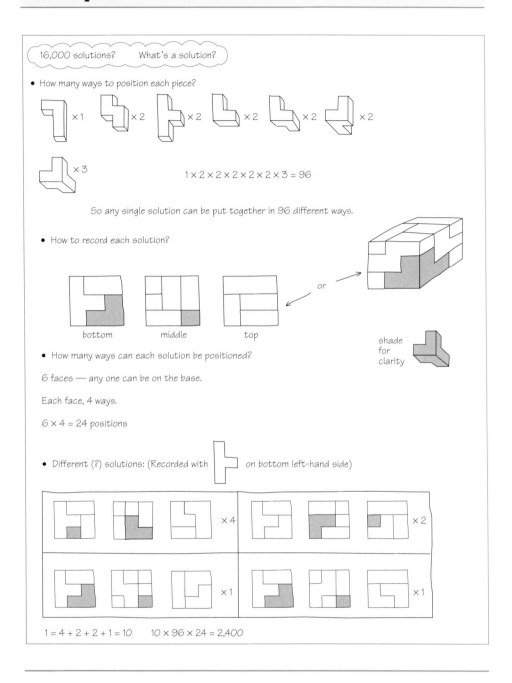

16,000 solutions?   What's a solution?

- How many ways to position each piece?

×1   ×2   ×2   ×2   ×2   ×2

×3

$$1 \times 2 \times 2 \times 2 \times 2 \times 2 \times 3 = 96$$

So any single solution can be put together in 96 different ways.

- How to record each solution?

bottom   middle   top

or

shade
for
clarity

- How many ways can each solution be positioned?

6 faces — any one can be on the base.

Each face, 4 ways.

$6 \times 4 = 24$ positions

- Different (?) solutions: (Recorded with ⊢ on bottom left-hand side)

×4   ×2

×1   ×1

$1 = 4 + 2 + 2 + 1 = 10$ $10 \times 96 \times 24 = 2,400$

No doubt you will have found parts of this mathematical writing puzzling. It would certainly not gain full marks if handed in as part of an assignment for this course! In some places, the writer does not make clear exactly what he means, so as a piece of mathematical communication it does not work. However, the author was not intending to communicate with anyone other than himself. It was a means for him to record his solution to a problem he had set himself and as such it may have been useful and successful.

Why were you asked to try to understand some mathematics which was not clearly written? There will be times (hopefully not too many!) during this course when you will not immediately be able to follow a mathematical argument. In such circumstances it is very easy for your mind to boggle at the complexity of it all and to give up, feeling that you cannot understand any of it.

In Activity 8 you were asked to 'make a note of the point when it becomes very difficult to understand'. Identifying precisely the actual cause of the misunderstanding is often a means of overcoming the difficulty. One technique that you might like to try in some circumstances is to go through the text, ticking line by line as you are able to follow an argument and marking clearly the point at which it is no longer clear. Then skip on a bit and see if there are lines further down the page where it is possible to follow the argument and tick those too. Then go back up the text and gradually you should be able to whittle away at the lines where there is lack of clarity. Eventually, the light may dawn completely, or you will have located a particular point which can subsequently be raised with your tutor.

You may be wondering why anyone would want to spend time trying to solve a problem like the one in Example 3. Often, in the real world, problems arise that need to be solved—but this is not the case here. Rather it is one of a class of real-world problems that are provoked by curiosity rather than necessity. As your mathematical confidence grows, you may experience a greater curiosity about the world and a willingness to apply new-found mathematical skills to problems that you have posed for yourself. In Section 1.3, you will return to this theme, as you listen to some mathematical musings in which curiosity about the world plays an important part.

In Example 3, as has been already pointed out, one aspect of the problem was finding a suitable way of recording solutions on paper or, in other words, of developing a suitable notation. The author chose an essentially geometrical representation in which the different two-dimensional drawings represented various three-dimensional arrangements. It is possible to conceive all sorts of different recording systems; for example, labelling each of the seven pieces of the puzzle with a different letter or using some kind of three-dimensional coordinate system. The general point here is that often in mathematical problem solving the problem solver has to decide which symbols will be most appropriate. Frequently it is algebraic symbols that are used, as with the formidable-looking Example 4!

Trying to understand this example is like trying to understand something written in a foreign language. You need to be familiar with the many symbols and signs in the same sort of way as you need to be familiar with the basic words of a language.

In this example there are symbols and signs, many of which you may not understand at present. Here are explanations of some of the symbols used in Example 4. Don't worry if you are unable to understand all the details.

> The letters d, h and x are being used to stand for the lengths of the sides of a triangle. Each one can take any sensible value—the letters are known as **variables**.

> The Greek letter θ (theta) is also being used as a **variable**, representing the size of one of the angles of the triangle—Greek letters are often used to stand for angles.

> Subscripts are used to indicate two different but related values: for example, g_1 and g_2 (say g-one, g-two) represent two different gradients.

> Superscripts are used to represent powers—in particular here d^2 means d to the power of 2 or d squared.

> $\dfrac{h}{x}$ means h divided by x, just as the fraction $\frac{1}{4}$ is the same as 1 divided by 4.

> Where two letters are written together it means their values are to be multiplied. For example, xg_1 is shorthand for x times g_1.

> tan and sin (say sine) stand for the trigonometric ratios, tangent and sine. Notice sin is not shorthand for s times i times n.

> $=$ is used to denote equality. Where it occurs at the beginning of a line it means the expression that follows is the equivalent of the one above.

> Brackets have been used, along with the superscript 2, to indicate that everything in the bracket has been squared. For example, $\left(\dfrac{h}{g_1}\right)^2$ is read as 'h divided by g_1 all squared'.

> Several equations have been labelled ((1), (2), and so on) so that they can be referred to later.

Example 4

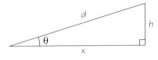

Let map gradient = g_1

$$= \frac{h}{x} \quad \text{①}$$

Let road gradient = g_2

$$= \frac{h}{d} \quad \text{②}$$

Also $g_1 = \tan\theta$ ③ $g_2 = \sin\theta$ ④

By Pythagoras' Theorem $d^2 = h^2 + x^2$ ⑤

From ① $g_1 = \frac{h}{x}$ so $xg_1 = h$ and $x = \frac{h}{g_1}$

From ② $g_2 = \frac{h}{d}$ so $dg_2 = h$ and $d = \frac{h}{g_2}$

Substitute into ⑤   to give

$$\left(\frac{h}{g_2}\right)^2 = h^2 + \left(\frac{h}{g_1}\right)^2$$

$$\frac{h^2}{g_2^2} = h^2 + \frac{h^2}{g_1^2}$$

Divide both sides by h^2

$$\frac{1}{g_2^2} = 1 + \frac{1}{g_1^2}$$

This shows that the gradients depend on each other
and not on the value of h.

Using ③ and ④

$$\frac{1}{(\sin\theta)^2} = 1 + \frac{1}{(\tan\theta)^2}$$

This equation contains only one variable, the angle θ.
It is independent of d, h and x.

Activity 9   *A good read*

Even though you will have little idea of what the symbols represent at the moment, it is still useful to practise reading them. Read Example 4 aloud to yourself, or impress someone else by reading it to them. Remember that what you are doing is similar to reading a passage from a foreign language. As you read, try to appreciate the patterns in the symbols and begin to appreciate the underlying story. Try to read with confidence—pretend that you speak mathematics like a native!

Now that you have read this formidable page of algebra you may feel a little more comfortable with the 'look' of symbols. But what does it all mean? For the answer to that question you will have to wait a few months. By the time you have studied as far as *Unit 9*, you should be able to read and use this sort of mathematical language with real understanding.

1.3   *What is a mathematician?*

In Section 1.2 you looked in detail at four pieces of very different mathematical writing:

> an investigation of patterns within our system of numbers;

> mathematical diagrams being used to convey statistical information about the real world;

> a solution of a geometrical problem which arose from someone's curiosity;

> use of algebraic symbols.

The aim was to broaden your experience of the sorts of situations where mathematics is used to help you develop your own understanding of what mathematics is. The examples were drawn from different areas of mathematics (arithmetic, statistics, geometry, algebra) and introduced ideas that will be developed further throughout the course.

Now you are asked to turn your attention to the question of what it means to be a mathematician. Recall the responses made to this question by the people you saw in the Whittington Hospital on the video band in Section 1.1. Does it simply mean someone who does mathematics? Or is it someone who uses it? Or is there more to it? How does a mathematician 'see' the world?

Activity 10   Stressing and ignoring

Read the Reader article 'Cabbages are not spheres' which is taken from a novel by William Boyd. Part of the conversation between the two characters, John and Hope, concerns how humans can look at one thing and see it in terms of something else.

Mark or make a note of any sentences or ideas which strike you as illustrating a mathematician's view of the world.

The Reader extract draws a distinction between the objects of the physical world around us and the 'objects' of mathematics: for instance, cones, spheres and straight lines. Yet for mathematics to be of use in solving problems in the physical world, it must also be possible to see these physical and mathematical objects as being the same thing under certain circumstances. Instead of *stressing* the differences, it can be important at times to *ignore* the differences; to be able to see cabbages as spheres, mountains as triangles, and rivers as flowing in straight lines. Thus particular features of the physical objects are *stressed* while others are *ignored*—with a cabbage, in some situations, its near spherical shape can be stressed while features like its colour, its stalk and its taste can be ignored. Seeing what to stress and what to ignore in particular circumstances is a key part of being a mathematician.

Mrs Johnson began to regret introducing the 'cabbages as spheres' metaphor to the rest of the family

Another necessary component of developing a mathematical view of the world is being able to recognize mathematical 'things'—shapes, curves, numbers, graphs, equations, and so on. Yet another element is developing a curious, questioning attitude towards the world around you. Why is that the way it is? Could it be different? If so, how? What if it were slightly different? Why isn't it different? What are the forces operating to make it the way it is? How can I describe the relationships I see?

Do people who study mathematics view the world and think about things any differently from other people? To find out whether there is a distinctively mathematical outlook on life, a member of the course team noted down things that set off a train of thought which could be described (in a broad sense) as mathematical. You can hear the result on band 1 of CDA5508.

Activity 11 *A mathematical muse*

Listen to band 1 of CDA5508 (Track 1) called 'Mathematical musings'.

The speaker describes a number of everyday things and occurrences which she sees as having interesting mathematical features. Make a note of the subjects described and any questions that interest you. Which elements mentioned do you find easy to see as mathematical and which are harder to see that way?

Over the coming week, try to cultivate your own 'mathematical eye and ear', looking out for ways in which mathematics permeates the various things you do, see and hear.

So, what is mathematics? And what is a mathematician? An aim of this first section of the first unit of the course was to help you begin to answer these questions. However, as you gain more experience of doing mathematics, your own understanding of the words will probably change. So press on with the course and see how your understanding develops.

Outcomes

Now that you have completed your work on this section, you should have:

◇   clarified your own ideas of what mathematics is and what it is to be a mathematician (Activities 1–5, 10 and 11);

◇   gained experience in working from DVD and audio CD as part of your mathematical learning (Activities 4 and 11);

◇   begun to recognize different types of written mathematics (Activities 6–9);

◇   developed your skill at reading mathematics (Activity 9);

◇   become more attuned to noticing mathematical questions arising from the world around you (Activities 3, 4, 10 and 11).

2 *Tapping into your calculator*

Aims   The aims of this section are for you to:

◇   gain greater fluency, confidence and skill in using your calculator;

◇   begin to appreciate how the calculator can be used as a tool for learning mathematics;

◇   develop an effective means of working from the *Calculator Book*.

◇

Ever since recorded mathematics began, people have been making use of mathematical aids. Four thousand years ago, Babylonian scribes were consulting mathematical tables which included multiplication tables, tables of squares and square roots, and tables of reciprocals of numbers. These values were recorded as marks on clay tablets that were then baked hard in the sun—and some have survived to the present day. (There are several originals to be seen in the British Museum.)

The reciprocal of a number is the number divided into 1. For example, the reciprocal of 5 is $\frac{1}{5}$, or 0.2.

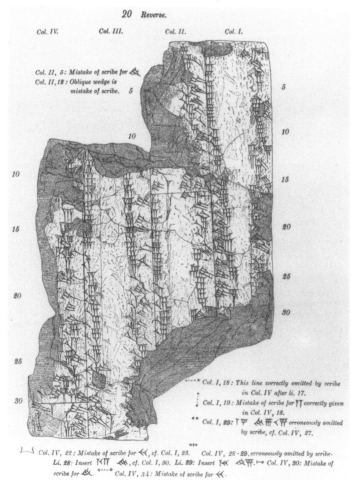

Plate depicting a Babylonian multiplication table tablet which shows encription errors made by scribes

The television programme 'Wood, brass and baboon bones' is about a broad range of mathematical devices that have been used through the ages.

Your calculator is one of the latest in a long and distinguished history of devices that have been invented to assist with the *doing* of mathematics. The list includes mathematical tables (stored on clay, papyrus, vellum and paper), the abacus and counting board, the slide rule, mechanical adding machines, and basic four-function electronic calculators. Some students will recall using a slide rule themselves (or seeing others working with them); others may remember using logarithm tables at school or work; still others may have had no exposure to either of them. Mathematical devices and calculating aids come and go.

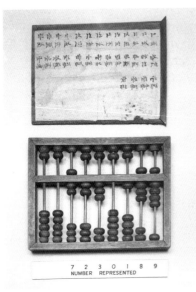

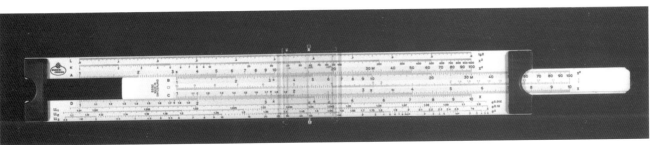

Three calculating aids: Chinese abacus, Brunsviga calculating machine and slide rule

On this course you will be using an electronic device known as a *graphics calculator*. It is capable not only of carrying out calculations but also of drawing graphs and other diagrams, of processing large amounts of statistical data and of carrying out pre-programmed sequences of instructions. There is a great deal of history in your calculator. Hundreds of years of mathematical activity and past thoughts of many people in different cultures have gone into producing and refining the ideas that are coded within this device. And all those human resources are available to you.

Many people see calculators only as a way of producing answers—indeed some people see them almost as a means of cheating, of short-cutting procedures that can and should be carried out in one's head or on paper. However, the calculator can also be a means of learning mathematics more effectively, something you will come to appreciate more as the course progresses. Many thousands of previous MU120 students have found that their graphics calculator, used with understanding and intelligence, has become a most effective aid to their learning. Many also say that using the calculator has been great fun!

By the end of the course you should know *how* to use many, but not all, of the mathematical features available on the calculator. Much more importantly, you should *understand* the mathematics associated with those features and know *when* it is appropriate to use them. For example, it is one thing to know *how* to work out the square root of a number using the calculator. It is quite another thing to *understand* what a square root is and *when* it is sensible to use it.

Your calculator will have been delivered along with the manufacturer's manual which describes how to use the various functions of the calculator. However, provided as part of the course materials, you also have the *Calculator Book*, which has been specially written for MU120. It serves two functions: to show you how to use the calculator and also to teach you the associated mathematics. You will probably only need to use the manufacturer's manual for reference purposes much later in the course.

You should have worked through the first four sections of Chapter 1 of the *Calculator Book* as part of the preparatory materials. If you have not yet done this, do it now before going on to the next activity.

Activity 12   *Glancing back*

Take a very quick look through Sections 1.1 to 1.4 of the *Calculator Book* and any notes you made when you studied the sections in your preparation. Ask yourself the following questions.

(a) What calculator skills were covered?

(b) What learning or revision of mathematical ideas was covered?
     Make notes on what you find.

In order to answer the questions in Activity 12, you may have used some or all of the following:

◇   the main headings in the text of the Calculator Book; for example, '1.2 Using the calculator for basic arithmetic';

◇   the sub-headings in the text, for example, 'Some calculator conventions';

◇   the diagrams—the representations both of the keyboard and of the calculator's screen (or 'screendumps');

◇   the single words in bold type in the margins, for example, **operation keys**, **inverse**, and so on;

◇   any highlighting, underlining or extra notes which you added to the text;

◇   any separate pages of notes which you may have made.

Why bother to point this out to you? The reason is that it is important to develop efficient and effective methods of studying (from a very early stage in the course). Certainly you need to 'do the mathematics' but there is also much to be gained from putting your own study methods and mathematical learning under the spotlight from time to time.

You were recommended to look back over, to see again or revise, work you had completed before. How useful were the notes you made? Were they too detailed or too sparse? Ideas about note-taking were covered in detail in Section 4.2 of *Preparing for Open Mathematics*. You might like to have another look at that section now before moving on the next activity.

Activity 13   *Glancing ahead*

Take a very quick look through Section 1.5 of the *Calculator Book*, entitled 'Everyday calculations'. Do not read it all yet!

Use the headings, subheadings, diagrams, and so on to give yourself an overview of what the section is about. In particular, ask yourself the following questions.

(a) Are there many new calculator skills?

(b) What new mathematical ideas are covered?

(c) What sorts of activities are required of me?

(d) How long will it take me?

Just as glancing back is a very useful study skill, so too is glancing ahead as it sets the ensuing work into context. It may take only a few seconds to complete but you need to be quite disciplined in order to do it—there's usually an almost overwhelming urge to press on with the actual study.

So, now that you have glanced ahead, ... press on!

Activity 14   *A pressing engagement*

Work through Section 1.5 of the *Calculator Book*. As you do so, bear in mind what you decided about the notes you made for the earlier sections—will you annotate the text itself in the margin, or do you need fuller, separate notes?

In Section 1.5 you are asked to complete four exercises. Do you need to write down the answers? If so, where and in how much detail? At what point should you check your answers with those at the back of the *Calculator Book?* When you have completed the section, glance back over the text and your notes, asking yourself what calculator skills and mathematical ideas were covered.

This section of the unit involves quite a lot of work from the *Calculator Book* and you may well not be able to complete it all in one study session. This may be a good point at which to assess how much time you have spent so far and how much work lies ahead. If you have not had a break since starting Section 2, why not take one now before you press on with the calculator?

Activity 15   *Pressing onwards*

(a) Work through Sections 1.6 and 1.7 of the *Calculator Book*, using the method suggested above of glancing ahead—pressing on—glancing back, if you find it useful.

(b) A number of important mathematical terms were introduced in Chapter 1 of the *Calculator Book*; for example, square, square root, reciprocal, and so on. Find the blue handbook sheet for *Unit 1* called 'Mathematical Terms' and make notes on each term listed (check back in the *Calculator Book* if you need to). Add notes on other important terms if you wish.

Towards the end of Section 1.7 of the *Calculator Book* there were three Brain stretchers. Usually these challenging puzzles and investigations can be regarded as optional, though desirable, extras. However, in this particular case, they are more important as they are linked to later work and may be part of the assessed work for the course. Go back and complete them now, if you haven't already done so. As you know, linked to each unit in MU120, there are assignments which give you the opportunity to test your understanding of the course materials. There are further details about these tutor-marked and computer-marked assignments (TMAs and CMAs) in Sections 7 and 8 of *Preparing for Open Mathematics* and you may well have already submitted the practice TMA and CMA linked to the preparatory materials.

When should you complete the assignment questions linked to each unit? Opinions differ about this. Some students find that it is better to leave the assignment questions until the end of the unit, while others prefer to complete parts of the assignments that are linked to specific parts of the text as they work through the unit. In the latter case you need to keep an eye on the assignment questions as you work through the text. Have a look at the assignment questions for *Unit 1* now and make a decision about when you will answer them. In later units you will have to decide both when you look at the assignment questions and when you decide to answer them.

Activity 16 Urgent assignment or not?

Find Assignment Booklet I in the course materials and read carefully the TMA and CMA questions that relate to *Unit 1*. Which of these questions are you in a position to answer now?

Decide whether to spend time now answering those questions or whether to return to complete them later.

Outcomes

Now that you have completed your work on this section, you should be able to:

◇   use the calculator for everyday calculations involving addition, subtraction, multiplication, division, and percentages (*Calculator Book*, 1.2 and 1.5);

◇   express numbers in scientific notation and understand how this notation is displayed by the calculator (*Calculator Book*, 1.6);

◇   understand the effect on a number entered on the calculator of the x-squared, square root, reciprocal and power keys (*Calculator Book*, 1.4 and 1.7);

◇   read simple mathematical expressions containing symbols such as $+$, $-$, $\times$, $\div$, $\sqrt{}$ and positive and negative powers (*Calculator Book*, 1.2 and 1.6);

◇   appreciate the idea of 'doing' and 'undoing' associated with pairs of specific keys on the calculator, and give some examples of common mathematical 'doing–undoing' pairs of operations (*Calculator Book*, 1.7).

3   *Studying mathematics*

 Aims   The aim of this section is to help you to think about how you study mathematics and consider ways in which you can make your study of the course more effective.   ◇

3.1   *Spotlight on study*

As you have been working through this unit, have you thought about *how* you are studying, and what this process involves? Do you feel confident or concerned about whether you will be able to learn the mathematics in this course and use it in the future? Put your study methods under the spotlight now, before moving on to *Unit 2*.

Learning rarely happens passively. A number of aspects of the course have been designed to encourage your more active participation and involvement. However, even that active experience may not be sufficient. There is a dangerous myth about 'learning from experience'. Of course, experience is necessary and important but it is seldom enough. Long-lasting learning comes about from *reflecting* on experience and integrating it into what you already know.

Think about how your own knowledge has developed on the course so far, in particular by concentrating on what you did in Section 2 of this unit. At the end of that section, like every section of the course, there was a list of 'outcomes'. One example of what you should have been able to do when you reached the end of that section was:

> express numbers in scientific notation, and understand how this notation is displayed by the calculator.

Such outcomes should provide you with a stimulus to reflect on what you have done—to think, for example, 'Am I sure what that means? How confident am I about doing that?' Sometimes your response will not be totally clear-cut. For example, you may think 'I am pretty confident about using scientific notation, at least for big numbers' or 'I think I understand what the calculator notation looks like'. The key point is to use the lists of outcomes to help you put your understanding under the spotlight.

Some activities in the course require a written response to some task or question. For example, in the last exercise in Chapter 1 of the *Calculator Book* you were asked to write down an explanation of some mathematical terms for somebody else. It is one thing to have some vague understanding of a particular mathematical concept and quite another to be able to describe it in words. Activities like this are designed to help you deepen your understanding and, although not everyone finds this sort of writing easy, it can be a valuable tool and is a skill well worth developing. Such written explanations will also be useful as reference for you later in the course.

Timothy's love letters took a new turn when he started studying MU120

Most of the learning that takes place in everyday life happens through a combination of theory and practice. For example, learning to make bread involves some theory (such as knowing what activates the yeast) and some practice (knowing when the dough has been kneaded sufficiently). So, learning involves making a connection between knowing (the *theory*) and doing (the *practice*).

Similarly, learning on this course requires both theory and practice to be present. The theory on its own is not sufficient. The ideas or theories have to be practised in real situations to see how they work. Similarly the practice—that is, mathematical activities, exercises and assignments—is not sufficient on its own. Without reflection or critical thinking, thorough learning will not result. It is when you think carefully about the activities and exercises that you can start to form general rules or theories.

'Good judgement comes from experience and experience comes from bad judgement', Barry Lepatner.

Writing about your own experience can be a very powerful way of learning from it because it helps you to stand back and move from the practice to the theory. The next activity asks you to do some more reflective writing, not this time about a particular mathematical topic but rather about your experience of study so far. Here you are putting your study methods under the spotlight.

Activity 17   *Studying study*

Find the cream-coloured activity sheet for this activity. You may like to use this sheet to help you structure your writing, but if you prefer you can use a method which suits you better.

Describe your experience of study on MU120 so far. Make brief notes under each of the headings which are also listed below. **Don't spend more than 10 minutes on this activity.**

◇   How did you get started? For example, at one extreme you may have just sat down, opened the books and got on with it, or at the opposite extreme you may have organized your working space carefully and sat down at pre-planned times.

◇   What have you enjoyed? For example, it may be the calculator work, or the chance to stretch your mind again, or it may be the different approach to mathematics.

◇   What practical problems have you faced so far? For example, you may have found it hard to concentrate; you may have suddenly realized that you needed to fetch an audio-cassette player or get the calculator.

◇ What have you learned from this? For example, is it best to plan
   study sessions at particular times of day, is it best to organize the
   study resources you need in advance, and so on?

Becoming more aware of how you go about studying allows you to monitor
and improve your approach and study methods. If you discuss Activity 17
with other students, friends or family members, you may see that
individuals differ enormously in how they go about studying.

To be effective, study must be organized so that it suits both your own life
style and your own preferred learning methods. People differ in how they
learn, how they approach solving problems and how they process
information. Try to become more aware of the learning methods and study
skills that suit you. In MU120, you will find a number of activities which
encourage you to do just this.

3.2 Keeping a record: a learning file

The term *learning file* is used throughout the course to mean a record of
your work in some sort of filing system. This may consist of a file, a box,
note books, a filing cabinet, files on your computer or something else that
suits you. You could consider including in your learning file items such as
your tutor's details (name, address, telephone number), stop presses,
activity sheets, assignment booklets, and any letters from the university
about this course. Your learning file may also be a good place to keep your
marked assignments containing your tutor's comments. Whatever the
content, you will certainly need some way of organizing your written notes
so that they stay together and in order.

Gradually, Snowy began to develop a taste for algebra

What sorts of notes will you need to keep? Now that you have almost completed *Unit 1*, you may have noticed that the activities are of different kinds. During the course, you will meet at least four different types of activities and will produce different sorts of written responses for each.

Exercises involve you working out a mathematical calculation or practising a particular technique. You have already completed several of these as you worked through Chapter 1 of the *Calculator Book*. Exercises are useful in helping you to develop and become confident in a particular skill or technique: some you will be able to complete quickly, whereas others will be more demanding. You may keep these responses in your learning file as a record of your working, or you may choose to do a calculation, for example, in the margin of the text. However, piles of odd pieces of paper without any date or reference are of little future use at all.

Investigations are primarily concerned with solving problems or puzzles. Here you will be involved in using and applying mathematics, that you have learned in a different situation, or to answer a particular question. The investigations (in certain units and particularly the Brain stretchers in the *Calculator Book*) should help you to assess how well you understand particular topics as well as giving you practice in a variety of mathematical techniques and skills. Some are quite short, while others will take longer to work through.

Handbook activities are concerned with writing notes on specific mathematical topics and terms. These activities have an icon next to the corresponding activity heading to indicate that they have blue activity sheets. As you complete these activities, you will be creating your own mathematical handbook or dictionary. You may find that the sheets are best kept as a useful reference source in a separate section of your learning file. There were some handbook sheets associated with the preparatory work for the course with the entries already filled in. The sheets linked to the first few units include the names of important new terms so that you can make notes on them. Feel free to add other notes of your own.

Study-skill activities are intended to help you think about, evaluate, and improve your own learning and performance in mathematics. You have just completed one of these, Activity 17. These activities also have an icon next to the activity heading to indicate that they have a cream-coloured activity sheet. Do not worry about completing all the space on the sheets—they are only designed as a guide. Brief notes to remind yourself are fine; they are intended as a periodic check on your progress, not as notes that will take hours to complete. None of them needs to take you more than 20 minutes to do. You may find it useful to keep the completed sheets in a separate section of your learning file.

Your responses to all four types of activity are designed to help you in preparing for the assessment on the course, but they will not be directly assessed, so they do not need to be perfectly presented; they are merely working notes for you. The printed activity sheets are designed to be useful to you, but if you prefer to organize your work differently, perhaps writing in a note book or on a computer, then feel free to do so.

Activity 18   *Organizing your learning file*

If you have not already done so, collect together all the written work you have produced so far, pages of answers to exercises and investigations, activity sheets, any stop presses and your Assignment Booklet.

Decide what your learning file should consist of. Organize it in a way that is useful and easy for you to use.

3.3   Skills in learning mathematics

A great deal has already been said about the study skills that you will be developing as you work through the course. But how might these help you in your future study, in the workplace or in any voluntary work that you do? This is the subject of the second band of the audio CD.

Activity 19   *Identifying skills*

Listen to band 2 of CDA5508 (Tracks 2–3), entitled 'Skills in learning mathematics'. As you listen you may wish to make some notes, and at one point you will be asked to stop the band in order to draw up a list of skills that you have been using and developing in the course so far. In the last part of the band, a former MU120 student speaks about some of the skills that he developed during his study of the course and how he has been able to use them since.

As you work through Open Mathematics, you will gain experience at identifying which aspects of your work you want to develop and improve, as well as how to assess and review your own performance. This can also be described as acquiring study skills.

Much of this section has involved looking at how you study and making learning more explicit. Many people can improve the effectiveness of their learning if they spend some time focusing not only on the content of what they are trying to learn, but also on the learning process itself. Even if you do not find any particular difficulties with studying, it is important to pause regularly to evaluate how well you are doing and whether you can learn more effectively by changing your approach. To this end, before you finish this unit, there is one more study-skills activity to complete.

Activity 20   *On reflection*

Find the cream-coloured activity sheet entitled 'On reflection'. Think about your first unit of study and, if you feel it is helpful, make brief notes on the sheet. Consider how many hours you have studied, the pattern of your study periods, and where and when you have studied.

Remember that *Unit 1* has been a short unit—most of the others will take you roughly twice as long to complete. Do you feel that any changes to your way of studying are needed as you start *Unit 2?*

Outcomes

Now that you have completed your work on this section, you should have:

◇   organized your learning file (Activity 18);

◇   reviewed the way that you are studying the course so far and begun to think about improvements (Activities 17 and 19).

Unit summary and outcomes

This unit introduced the varied components of the course that you will use to learn mathematics: a calculator, reader articles, audio and video bands. You have mainly been working from this course text and *Calculator Book*.

A number of activities involved communicating your ideas: the meaning of mathematical terms; where you can 'see' mathematics in everyday settings; reviewing how you have studied this material. Writing is one aspect of communication which is central to learning. So it makes sense for you to think about and develop your skills in this area.

Part of learning mathematics is to learn to speak and think like a mathematician: becoming more aware of and fluent with the language of mathematics.

As you have now completed this first unit of work, take a few minutes to go through the list of outcomes and think about what you have achieved.

Outcomes

You should now:

◇　be able to describe your view of what mathematics is (Section 1);

◇　have begun to recognize different types of written mathematics and developed your skill at reading it (Activities 6–9);

◇　be able to tackle mathematical problems using a calculator (*Calculator Book*, Chapter 1);

◇　be able to use your calculator with understanding for basic arithmetic, percentages, square roots, reciprocals and powers (*Calculator Book*, Sections 1.2, 1.4, 1.5);

◇　be able to express and interpret numbers in scientific notation, both in writing and on your calculator (*Calculator Book*, Section 1.6);

◇　be able to give some examples of common mathematical 'doing–undoing' pairs of operations (*Calculator Book*, Section 1.7);

◇　be more attuned to noticing mathematical questions arising from the world around you (Activities 3, 4, 10 and 11);

◇　have increased experience in working from DVD and audio CD as part of your mathematical learning (Activities 4, 11 and 19);

◇　have organized and planned your study (Activities 12–19).

Assessed work

Do not forget that there are TMA and CMA questions associated with your work from this unit. If you have not already done so, it would be sensible to complete those questions before moving on to *Unit 2*.

Comments on Activities

Activity 1

Of course, there is no single right answer to this activity as your response will depend entirely on your memories of your own experience at school.

Some people might have marked the following sentence as one with which they agreed:

> The teacher pretended that algebra was a perfectly natural affair, to be taken for granted, whereas I didn't even know what numbers were.

However, one person reading this underlined the word 'pretended', and wrote in the margin—'The teacher wasn't pretending! I expect for him, as for me, algebra did seem a perfectly natural affair.'

Here are some other parts of the article which have particular significance for some people.

> Oddly enough my class mates could handle these things ...

> I finally grasped that what was aimed at was a kind of system of abbreviation, with which many quantities could be put into a short formula.

> Equations I could comprehend only by inserting specific numerical values in place of the letters ...

> I was so intimidated by my incomprehension that I did not dare to ask any questions.

Activity 2

Again, this activity has no right or wrong answers. You were asked to do two things: some thinking (mainly using your memory) and some writing. You will know whether you responded to both these requests as thoroughly as possible.

In this case you might have found it useful to do the writing on a separate sheet of paper, or perhaps you squeezed it into the margin beside the main text in the unit.

Here are some contrasting ways in which people have completed the sentence: 'During my school years, I came to see that mathematics was ...'

... a subject which I found intriguing, challenging and sometimes confusing.

... to be avoided as much as possible.

... fun!

... going to be useful in my work as a nurse.

Activity 3

In this activity you were not asked to write anything—the activity required here was simply to think. Of course, there is no reason why you should not have made some notes or answered the questions in writing, and indeed this may have helped you to ensure that you really engaged with the questions asked. It is all too easy to give such questions only cursory thought, whereas the discipline of writing ensures that your thinking is active and purposeful.

An alternative way of ensuring that you engage fully is to speak your answers out loud. If there is a friend or member of the family who is willing to listen it can be very helpful, but otherwise many OU students have found that household pets make good listeners! Either way, writing or speaking your answers will certainly help you maintain an active learning style.

One person discussed this activity with their partner and together they came up with the following list of occasions when they had been subconsciously using mathematics during one weekend spent visiting parents.

◇ Estimating what time to leave home in order to arrive in time for lunch.

◇ Comparing petrol prices.

◇ Calculating (roughly) the cost of coffees when they stopped at the service station—did they have enough cash?

◇ Working out how long it had been since we saw a distant member of the family.

◇ Estimating how much water to put in an unfamiliar teapot.

◇ Discussing with parents ways of increasing the interest they get on their savings.

◇ Working out whether there was enough wood of the right size in the garage to put up extra shelves.

◇ Sharing the cost of a meal in a restaurant.

◇ Planning an alternative route home in order to avoid roadworks on the motorway.

Activity 4

(a) Trevor Arnold talks about the need to estimate and measure distances, areas and times. The spreadsheet he created uses hidden formulas which instruct the computer to carry out the routine calculations that he previously did by hand.

Emma Prescott uses mathematics to help her estimate the drop of haemoglobin levels in her patients. By recording how far levels have fallen, she is able to predict when the next blood transfusion will be necessary. She also calculates necessary drug dosages and volumes of intravenous infusions. She uses probability when explaining the likelihood of passing on the disease to a patients offspring. You will have seen her twice using simple diagrams to convey mathematical ideas—an important theme of this course.

Although Mark Hanson is not consciously using mathematics, he is using a range of mathematical skills as he schedules the time he has available, estimates the lengths of record tracks, subtracts them from the time available, and so on.

(b) When first asked about their attitudes to mathematics, the responses were fairly varied; some people had positive memories of school mathematics while others disliked it or found it boring. You may also have noticed that at the beginning of the video band most people viewed maths in a rather narrow way—in fact, they tended to see it simply as basic arithmetic applied to everyday situations. As the video unfolds, these perceptions of mathematics became extended. Indeed, all the hospital workers interviewed were prepared, by the end, to think of their jobs more mathematically than they had at the beginning of the video.

Whether or not the views expressed are similar to yours, they may well seem to be typical of the population as a whole. However, this is just a small selection of people and it was not chosen as a representative sample of the whole population. They all came from one particular hospital in one particular area in London. Can you be sure that people's views of mathematics are not influenced by the circumstances of the interview or the nature of their job or the area in which they live? These ideas involving the biased nature of certain samples are developed further in *Unit 4*.

(c) You may care to read again the comments about using video that were given before Activity 4.

Activity 5

In Example 1 it is the use of many **numbers** that identifies it as mathematics and suggest the area of mathematics called *arithmetic*. Example 2 has numbers but also **graphs and diagrams**, suggesting *statistics*. The **shapes** in Example 3 suggest that the *geometrical* part of mathematics is being used whereas Example 4, with all the **alphabetic symbols**, is clearly drawing upon *algebra*.

Activity 6

There are no comments on this activity because each student's response will be very personal.

Activity 7

'What's in your dustbin' (the pie chart) shows the percentage of packaging materials in an average UK dustbin: 7.5% glass, 5% paper, and so on. It also shows that 75.25% is non-packaging.

'How much is recycled' (the line graph) shows that the percentage of materials recycled is increasing. It is highest for glass, at 60%, and lowest for plastics and paper (about 10%). Notice, however, that the horizontal scale is not evenly spaced. Does this distort the graph unreasonably?

'German ambition' (a bar chart) shows Germany's aim to collect and recycle different materials. Although comparisons between the different materials are shown, it does not make clear what the percentages are part of. For example, 60% of what glass is collected?

'How much' (a bar chart) shows the quantity of packaging materials used in the UK (in millions of tons); paper (industrial) is the largest.

'Could do better' (a bar chart) compares the percentage of glass recycled in different Western European countries in 1992. The Netherlands is highest at about 75%; the UK and Greece are low with about 20%.

Activity 8

You may find the following explanation of the writing helpful (in conjunction with the copy of Example 3 printed opposite), but there are comments about the activity in the main text.

The first bullet point tackles the problem of what is meant by a 'solution'. Imagine all seven pieces have been combined to make a cube. Now imagine taking a single piece out and seeing whether that piece can be re-inserted in any different ways. The first piece pictured can be positioned in only one way, whereas the piece next to it could be turned round and put back upside down. This is to do with the symmetry of the piece (see 'Preparatory Resource Book B', Module 7). The number of ways each piece can be inserted in any cube has been noted: 1, 2, 2, 2, 2, 2 and 3. These numbers are then multiplied to give 96, the total number of different ways of putting the pieces together to form any single cubic arrangement.

The second bullet point tackles the problem of how to record a particular cubic arrangement. The three-dimensional picture of the cube is easy to visualize but difficult to draw. It also does not record the position of pieces on the far side of the cube. The author is experimenting with a notation where the three horizontal layers of the cube are drawn side by side but there are then problems visualizing the individual pieces.

In the third bullet point the author realises that any complete cubic arrangement of the seven pieces can be turned around in various ways (because of the symmetry of the cube). He reckons there are 24 ways of positioning each complete cubic arrangement.

Finally he begins to record some of what he thought originally were different solutions. Alongside the drawings he has written ×4, ×2, ×1, ×2, presumably indicating that he thinks there are 4, 2, 1 and 2 similar cubic arrangements to those illustrated but it is not clear from the writing what these are. The $1 + 4 + 2 + 2 + 1 = 10$ may be the total of these cubic arrangements (including 1 from the second bullet point). He then combines the 96 ways of putting the pieces together, with the 24 ways of positioning each complete cubic arrangement and multiplies by 10 the number of cubic arrangements. Counting like this, he seems to have found about 2,400 ways of completing the Soma Cube. Only another 14,000 or so to go!

Example 3

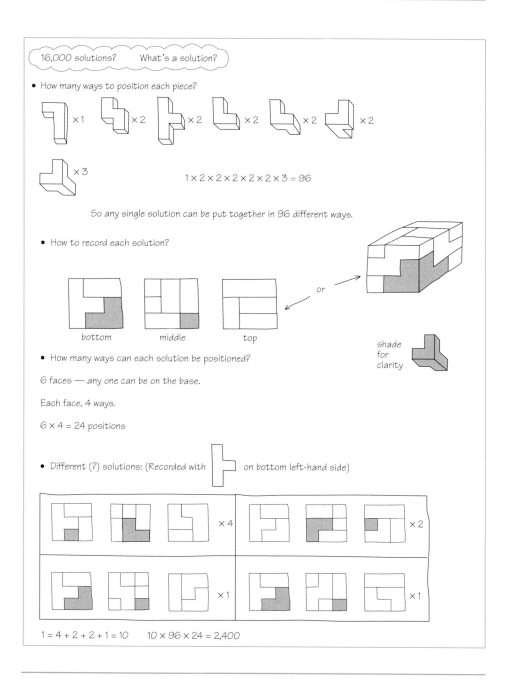

16,000 solutions?   What's a solution?

- How many ways to position each piece?

×1   ×2   ×2   ×2   ×2   ×2

×3   1 × 2 × 2 × 2 × 2 × 2 × 3 = 96

So any single solution can be put together in 96 different ways.

- How to record each solution?

bottom   middle   top

or

shade
for
clarity

- How many ways can each solution be positioned?

6 faces — any one can be on the base.

Each face, 4 ways.

6 × 4 = 24 positions

- Different (?) solutions: (Recorded with ⊤ on bottom left-hand side)

×4   ×2

×1   ×1

1 = 4 + 2 + 2 + 1 = 10   10 × 96 × 24 = 2,400

45

Activity 9

You may have begun like this:

Let the map gradient be g-*one* which equals h divided by x (Equation 1)...

About half-way down comes the more difficult line:

Substitute into Equation 5 to give,

'h divided by g-*two* all squared equals h-squared plus h divided by g-*one* all squared'.

Activity 10

A key sentence comes towards the end of the excerpt.

> The natural world is full of irregularity and random alteration, but in the antiseptic, dust-free, shadowless, brightly lit, abstract realm of the mathematicians they like their cabbages spherical, please.

There are further comments about the article in the main text.

Activity 11

Below is a list of the topics referred to in the audio band. You will meet all those marked with an asterisk in later course units.

Saturday:	Guitar frets(*), think-of-a-number games(*), clock arithmetic.
Sunday:	Formula for the age of a tree(*), daylight length(*).
Monday:	Cauliflorets (self similarity*).
Tuesday:	Graphs in a newspaper(*),
Wednesday:	How many translators?
Thursday:	Phone bill, Time zones, Types of maps(*).
Friday:	OU Logo(*), rainbows(*)

Activity 12

You may have included all or some of these and you might have a few extra ones.

(a) Calculator skills

> Adjusting display contrast;
> Turning on/off and resetting memory;
> Using the main and second function keys;
> Very basic arithmetic $+$, $-$, $\times$ and $\div$;
> Editing an expression and use of the cursor keys;
> Inputting negative numbers;
> Setting the number of decimal places;
> Being aware of calculator conventions and the use of brackets;
> Interpreting error messages;
> Use of the MODE menu;
> Use of square and power keys.

(b) Mathematical ideas covered

> Inverse operations;
> Decimal places;
> Negative numbers;
> Order of operations;
> Sequences and converging to a limit (see Brain stretcher in Section 3);
> Squares, square roots and other powers.

There are further comments about this activity in the main text.

Activity 13

(a) There are only two new calculator skills: storing numbers and entering alphabetic characters.

(b) Percentage increases and decreases, including working with VAT;
Comparing price rises;
Conducting an investigation;
Estimation.

(c) *Calculating* using the calculator and *checking* calculations;
Following instructions, especially those involving key sequences;
Recalling earlier skills;
Comparing different values and methods; for example, with *practising* methods just introduced;

Making notes and *reflecting* on methods;
Investigating, which might involve some research;
Predicting and *estimating* to get a rough idea of the solution to a problem;
Interpreting results.

These activities can be divided roughly into 'doing exercises', 'using skills to work on a problem' and 'making notes'.

(d) The answer will vary from student to student, but it will clearly depend on how familiar you are with the use of percentages.

Activity 14

Some students like to see notes in the original context and so choose to annotate the text. Others like to make notes on cards so that they can be easily referenced—there are many alternatives. You need to decide on a method that will work well for you.

If you feel that the question requires a written answer then do not throw your solution away, but keep it for reference later. Remember that most of this writing will be seen only by you, so do not waste too much precious time on presentation.

When you have completed the section and glanced back to see what calculator skills and mathematical ideas were covered, you may like to compare the list of points in the comment to Activity 13(a) and (b), above with your points.

Activity 15

(a) There are many answers and comments relating to the exercises at the back of the Calculator Book.

(b) You could use the index to find terms, if necessary.

Activity 16

Some students feel that it is a better measure of their understanding if there is a period of time between completing their study and doing the assessed work. This may be true, but other students find that it is a more efficient use of time to answer questions as soon as they are in a position to do so. There is also an argument that answering assessed questions and looking for relevant material is actually a useful part of the learning process. Once again you need to think about your own preferred learning style and to develop a system for answering TMA and CMA questions that suits you.

Activity 17

There are comments about this activity in the main text.

Activity 18

There are no comments on this activity because your learning file will be organized in a way that suits you.

Activity 19

There are comments on the audio band itself relating to the activity you are asked to carry out.

Activity 20

There are no comments on this activity as each student will have their own view on how their learning has gone and on how best to adapt it to the study of future units.

Acknowledgements

Grateful acknowledgement is made to the following sources for permission to reproduce material in this unit:

Figures/illustrations/photographs

Example 2:*Guardian*, 10 January, 1994. Copyright ©1994 The Guardian; p. 28 photo by permission of The British Library (AC2692 p/20); p. 29: Copyright ©Science Museum/Science and Society Picture Library.

Cover

Guillemots: RSPB Photo Library; Sellafield newspaper headline: *Independent*, 8 January, 1993; other photographs: Mike Levers, Photographic Department, The Open University.

Index